In this story you will lea  vowel sound. Can you fir sound them out?

Sam   fast   carry   pal
can   catch   branch

Here are some review sight words:

a   is

Here are some new sight words:

too

Here are some fun words:

run   ball   woof   Biscuit   ruff   help

Sam can run fast.

Sam can catch a ball.

Sam can carry a branch.

Woof!
Can Biscuit carry
a branch, too?

Ruff!

Sam can help Biscuit.

Sam is
Biscuit's pal!